THE STONE ROSES
Second Coming

Breaking Into Heaven... 10

Driving South... 23

Ten Storey Love Song... 32

Daybreak... 36

Your Star Will Shine... 45

Straight To The Man... 50

Begging You... 68

Tightrope... 61

Good Times... 76

Tears... 90

How Do You Sleep... 84

Love Spreads... 99

Notation & Tablature Explained... 8

Sony Music Publishing Limited

Breaking Into Heaven

I've been casing your joint for the best years of my life,
Like the look of your stuff, outta sight.
When I'm hungry and when I'm cold,
When I'm having it rough or just getting old.
Listen up sweet child of mine, have I got news for you,
Nobody leaves this place alive, they'll die and join the queue.

Better man the barricades, I'm coming in tonight,
Had a line of my dust, outta sight.
When I wander and when I roam,
I'll find a soul I can trust, I'm coming home.
Listen up sweet child of mine, have I got news for you,
Nobody leaves this place alive, they'll die and join the queue, sing it.

I'm, I'm gonna break right into heaven,
I can't wait anymore.

Heaven's gates won't hold me, I'll saw those suckers down,
Laughing loud at your locks when they hit the ground.
Every icon in every town,
Hear this, your number's up, I'm coming round.
Listen up sweet child of mine, have I got news for you,
Nobody leaves this place alive, they'll die and join the queue, sing it.

I'm, I'm gonna break right into heaven,
I can't wait anymore.

How many times will I have to tell you,
You don't have to wait to die,
You can have it all, anytime you want it,
Yeah, the kingdom's all inside.

Driving South

Driving south round midnight, man, I must have been insane,
Driving south round midnight in a howling hurricane.
I stopped for an old man hitcher at a lonely old crossroad,
He said, 'I'm going nowhere, I'm only here to see if I can steal your soul.'

'I'm not tryin' to make you, I don't want to touch your skin,
I know all there is to know about you and all your sins.
Well, you ain't too young or pretty, and you sure as hell can't sing,
Anytime you want to sell your soul, I've got a toll-free number you can ring.'

'I'm not tryin' to make you, I don't want to touch your skin,
I know all there is to know about you and all your sins.
Well, you ain't too young or pretty, and you sure as hell can't sing,
Anytime you want to sell your soul, I've got a toll-free number you can ring.'

O eight O O triple six, oh yeah.
O eight O O triple six, oh yeah.

I stopped for an old man hitcher at a lonely old crossroad,
He said, 'I'm going nowhere, I'm only here to see if I can steal your soul.'

Ten Storey Love Song

When your heart is black and broken and you need a helping hand,
When you're so much in love you don't know just how much you can stand,
When your questions go unanswered, and the silence is killing you,
Take my hand baby, I'm your man, I got loving enough for two.

Ten storey love song, I built this thing for you, ooh.
Who can take you higher than twin peak mountain blue?
Oh well, I built this thing for you, and I love you true.

There's no sure-fire set solutions, no short cut through the trees,
No breach in the wall that they put there to keep you from me.
As you're lying awake in this darkness, this everlasting night,
Someday soon, don't know where or when, you're gonna wake up and see the light.

Ten storey love song, I built this thing for you, ooh.
Who can take you higher than twin peak mountain blue?
Oh well, I built this thing for you, and I love you true.

Ten storey love song, I built this thing for you, ooh.
Who can take you higher than twin peak mountain blue?
Oh well, I built this thing for you, and I love you true.

Daybreak

This is the daybreak, and this is the love we make, for love is the law here.
You've got to know how I love it, yeah, it's more than a mover,
You know it takes all fast, all song, stone cold wild.
Bring the love in son, brother, man, true nature child.
I think I'll sing it.

From Atlanta Georgia, to Longside Manchester,
Everyone ready, so, so willing and able, yeah, yeah, yeah,
For the love you make, gone 'ome sis', huh, yeah, wooh!

She built it to make ya, we all love makers ain't we?
Sister Rosa Lee Parks, love forever her name in your heart,
Forever in my heart, mm, yeah, woh, hey!

As I sing on this song, someone just got rolled on, hey, oh hey, yeah, wooh yeah.

New York City to Addis Ababababa,
Keep on keeping strong, keep on keeping on.

So why no stack for black on a radio station in this, the city?
Been going on so long, level on the line, I'm a leaf on the vine of time.
Black bones are the original bones,
And so this the whole wide world should know, y'all.
I came to sing this song in your city.
Ooh, for the dreamers, one more for the dreamers, yeah.

Your Star Will Shine

Your star will shine again one day, through deep blue velvet skies,
Shine for all the world to see the universe in your eyes.

When the storm outside is raging, and the dogs, they howl your name,
Lay down, sleep, and I'll kiss you, your star will shine again.
Hush my darling, don't you cry, I'll stay by your side until morning,
All through the night I'll watch the skies.

And your distant sun will shine
Like the gun that's trained right between your Daddy's eyes.

Straight To The Man

Saying this revelation, call delia station,
An initiation, all you'd better beware.
Who'll cast the first stone?
Skin to the bone, bring it all on home, bring it on for Jerome.
So, new castle, build a brand new castle, yeah, yeah, yeah, yeah, yeah,
Straight to the man.

On an island of traders, you know they're trying to fade ya,
No-one can train you, no-one evade you, no-one can fade you,
Saying 'Don't be late, no, the train won't wait',
Saying 'Don't be late, no, the boat can't wait',
Saying, 'Don't be late, no, the train nor the boat or the train can't wait, yeah.'

Do the do, do the do, do the do do,
Do the do do, do the do do do,
Do the do do, do the do do do do do do do do do the, heading straight for the man.
Oh, you know they'll never evade you.

So now I stand here, love cuts down a revolver,
Am stern damn in Sodom and Gomorrah,
So I'm singing to King Stone, your teaching it's on.
They say it's a fable, though I was made able.
I slipped through the net, wanna bet it's a ramble, a sandstorm,
One slip you don't never forget, who could ever forget? You know I never forget.
Do do do, do do do, do do do do do do do, do do do do, straight to the man.
Oh, you know they're trying to fade you.

Saw this revelation, call delia station.
I don't need no powder, one kinder, easy blind ya,
Yeah, the ice of Grande Bretagne owes a debt,
Say, the ice of Grande Bretagne,
All the eyes of Grande Bretagne all the eyes of Grande Bretagne owes a debt.
Yeah, the eyes of Grande Bretagne all eyes of Grande Bretagne owes us a debt.

Begging You

I'm begging you,
I'm begging you.

The fly on the coachwheel told me that he got it and he knew what to do with it,
Everybody saw it, saw the dust that he made.
King bee in a frenzy, ready to blow, got the horn good to go wait,
Oh, his sting's all gone, now he's begging you, begging you.

Here is a warning, the sky will divide,
Since I took off the lid, now there's nowhere to hide,
Now I'm begging you, I'm begging you.
This is a mystery not to be solved,
But be minded, like minded, I'm gone,
Still I'm with you, I'm begging you, I'm begging you.

Give it over, give it over.
Give it over, give it begging you.
Give it over, give it over.
Give it over, yeah I'm begging you, I'm begging you.

Weigh it and say it, is it all in a name,
Does it call you or maul you and drive you insane.
Can it make you remember, time is in place,
Now I'm belling you, I'm begging you.

The fly on the coachwheel told me that he got it and he knew what to do with it,
Everybody saw it, saw the dust that he made.
Make all the dust that you can, make all the dust that you can.
King bee in a frenzy ready to blow.

Good Times

Hell hath no fury like a woman scorned.
I'll tell you my story man, I wish I'd never been born.
I'm loose at the seams, I've broken my dreams,
And my hand, it shakes the pen.
Come on, come on now, baby, let the good times roll again, yeah.

Where did our sweet love go? Who stole away our time?
Why do the stars above refuse to shine?
The harder I try to paint a picture of the way it was back then,
The more I miss the good times, baby, let it roll again.

Good times baby, this is the time I need to know that your love is mine,
Love me up yeah, reel me in,
I'm hooked, line and sinker, she's my heroin.

How many days have I been lying on my back
Staring at the ceiling girl, stretching on your rack?
The harder I try to paint a picture of the way it was back then,
The more I miss the good times, baby, let it roll again.

Good times baby, this is the time I need to know that your love is mine,
Love me up yeah, yeah, reel me in,
I'm hooked, line and sinker, she's my heroin.

Said I'm hooked now, I'm not fakin',
I'm here till the day I die.
Can't get enough now, my heart is aching,
I'm in too deep to stop, all I want is those
Good times baby, this is the time I need to know that your love is mine,
Love me up yeah, yeah, reel me in,
I'm hooked, line and sinker, she's my heroin.

Tightrope

You should have been an angel, it would've suited you.
My gold-leafed triptych angel, she knows just what to do.
In the half light of morning, in a world between the sheets,
I swear I saw her angel wing, my vision was complete.

And I know I'll never want another lover, my sweet,
Can there be more in this world than the joy of just watching you sleep?
I don't know just what to feel.
Won't someone tell me my love's real?

Are we etched in stone or just scratched in the sand,
Waiting for the waves to come and reclaim the land?
Will the sun shine all sweetness and light,
Burn us to a cinder, our third stone satellite?
I'm on a tightrope, baby, nine miles high,
Striding through the clouds, on my ribbon in the sky.
I'm on a tightrope, baby, one thing I've found,
I don't know how to stop, and it's a long, long, long, long way down.

She's all that ever mattered, and all that ever will,
My cup, it runneth over, I'll never get my fill.
The boats in the harbour, slip from their chains,
Head for new horizons, let's do the same.
I'm on a tightrope, baby, nine miles high,
Striding through the clouds, on my ribbon in the sky.
I'm on a tightrope, baby, one thing I've found,
I don't know how to stop, and it's a tightrope, baby, nine miles high,
Striding through the clouds, on my ribbon in the sky.
I'm on a tightrope baby, one thing I've found,
I don't know how to stop, and it's a long, long, long, long way down.

Tears

Our love, girl, is going through changes,
I don't know if I'm alive, dead, dying or just a little jaded,
Someone throw me a line.
You know I need it, I need it bad.

Lost in a maze of my own making,
No way out that I can find, send home your hard working jury,
I'm going down this time.
You better believe it, yes, you had.

So, if you hear me crying, or talking in my sleep,
Don't be afraid, it's just the hours that I keep.
We gotta love to last for a million years,
A love that could never fade through the tracks of your tears.
All I can do is hope that you will see me fall,
Do your best to smash my picture on your wall.
Forgive me baby, absolve me, my dear.
I've seen the future in the tracks of your tears.

I've seen the future in the tracks of your tears, of your tears, of your tears.

I cast a shorter shadow with every passing day,
No time to think, I'm just fading away.
Some kind of magic in all your hopes and fears,
Show me the future through the tracks of your tears.

How Do You Sleep

I've seen your severed head at a banquet for the dead,
All dressed up dinner, looked so fine.
Your shining silver slaver so tastefully powdered
With the finest military quick lime.

Now try and picture this, as I gave you a kiss,
The apple in your mouth slipped in mine.
The orchestra played the sweetest serenade,
We laughed as we put away your wine.

So raise your glasses, here's a toast to wasted lives.
May all their ghosts come back to haunt you,
And tell you how they died.

How do you sleep?
How do you last the night and keep the dogs at bay?
How do you feel when you close your eyes, and try and drift away?
Does it feel any better now?
Does it mean any more when the angel of death comes knock, knocking,
And banging at your door?

When all the fun was over, I put you on my shoulder,
Took you home, away from it all.
Shot down and claimed, mounted and framed,
Tastefully hung up on my wall.
Are my dreams your nightmares? I hope they all come true.
Get off your knees, the party's over,
I'm coming home to you.

How do you sleep?
How do you last the night and keep the dogs at bay?
How do you feel when you close your eyes, and try and drift away?
Does it feel any better now?
Does it mean any more when the angel of death comes knock, knocking,
And banging at your door, at your door?

Love Spreads

Love spreads her arms, waits there for the nails,
I forgive you, boy, I will prevail.
Too much to take, come cross to bear,
I'm hiding in the trees with a picnic, she's over there, yeah.

Yeah, yeah, yeah,
Yeah, yeah, yeah.

She didn't scream, she didn't make a sound,
'I forgive you, boy,' but don't leave town.
Cold black skin, naked in the rain,
Hammer flash in the lightning, they're hurting her again.

Let me put you in the picture, let me show you what I mean,
The messiah is my sister, ain't no king, man, she's my queen.
Let me put you in the picture, let me show you what I mean,
The messiah is my sister, ain't no king, man, she's my queen.
I have a dream, I've seen the light,
Don't put it out, say she's alright, yeah, she's my sister.

She didn't scream, she didn't make a sound,
'I forgive you, boy,' but don't leave town.
Cold black skin, naked in the rain,
Hammer flash in the lightning, they're hurting her again.
Oh, oh, ooh,
Yeah, yeah, yeah, yeah.

Let me put you in the picture, let me show you what I mean,
The messiah is my sister, ain't no king, man, she's my queen.
Let me put you in the picture, let me show you what I mean,
The messiah is my sister, ain't no king, man, she's my queen.
Let me put you in the picture, let me show you what I mean,
The messiah is my sister, ain't no king, man, she's my queen.
Let me put you in the picture, let me show you what I mean,
The messiah is my sister, ain't no king, man, she's my queen.
Let me put you in the picture, let me show you what I mean,
The messiah is my sister, ain't no king, man, she's my queen.
Let me put you in the picture, let me show you what I mean,
The messiah is my sister, ain't no king, man, she's my queen.
Let me put you in the trees in the picture, let me show you what I mean,
The messiah is my sister, ain't no king, man, she's my queen.
Let me put you in the picture, let me show you what I mean,
The messiah is my sister, ain't no king, man, she's my queen.
I have a dream, I've seen the light,
Don't put it out, say she's alright, yeah, she's my sister.

Notation & Tablature Explained

Open C chord

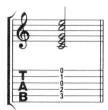

Scale of E major

High E (1st) string
B (2nd) string
G (3rd) string
D (4th) string
A (5th) string
Low E (6th) string

Bent Notes

The note fretted is always shown first. Variations in pitch achieved by string bending are enclosed within this symbol ⌐ ¬. If you aren't sure how far to bend the string, playing the notes indicated without bending gives a guide to the pitches to aim for. The following examples cover the most common string bending techniques:

Example 1
Play the D, bend up one tone (two half-steps) to E.

Example 4
Pre-bend: fret the D, bend up one tone to E, then pick.

Example 2
Play the D, bend up one tone to E then release bend to sound D. Only the first note is picked.

Example 5
Play the A and D together, then bend the B-string up one tone to sound B.

Example 3
Fast bend: Play the D, then bend up one tone to E as quickly as possible.

Example 6
Play the D and F♯ together, then bend the G-string up one tone to E, and the B-string up a semitone to G.

Additional guitaristic techniques have been notated as follows:

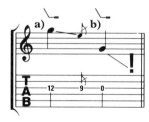

Tremolo Bar
Alter pitch using tremolo bar. Where possible, the pitch to aim for is shown.
a) Play the G; use the bar to drop the pitch to E.
b) Play the open G; use the bar to 'divebomb', i.e. drop the pitch as far as possible.

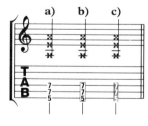

Mutes
a) Right hand mute
Mute strings by resting the right hand on the strings just above the bridge.
b) Left hand mute
Damp the strings by releasing left hand pressure just after the notes sound.
c) Unpitched mute
Damp the strings with the left hand to produce a percussive sound.

Hammer on and Pull off
Play first note, sound next note by 'hammering on', the next by 'pulling off'. Only the first note is picked.

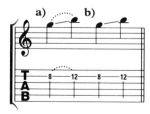

Glissando
a) Play first note, sound next note by sliding up string. Only the first note is picked.
b) As above, but pick second note.

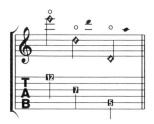

Natural Harmonics
Touch the string over the fret marked, and pick to produce a bell-like tone. The small notes show the resultant pitch, where necessary.

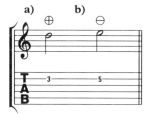

Slide Guitar
a) Play using slide.
b) Play without slide.

Artificial Harmonics
Fret the lowest note, touch string over fret indicated by diamond notehead and pick. Small notes show the resultant pitch.

Vibrato
Apply vibrato, by 'shaking' note or with tremolo bar. As vibrato is so much a matter of personal taste and technique, it is indicated only where essential.

Pinch Harmonics
Fret the note as usual, but 'pinch' or 'squeeze' the string with the picking hand to produce a harmonic overtone. Small notes show the resultant pitch.

Pick Scratch
Scrape the pick down the strings – this works best on the wound strings.

Microtones
A downwards arrow means the written pitch is lowered by less than a semitone; an upwards arrow raises the written pitch.

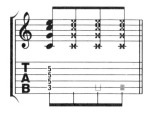

Repeated Chords
To make rhythm guitar parts easier to read the tablature numbers may be omitted when a chord is repeated. The example shows a C major chord played naturally, r/h muted, l/h muted and as an unpitched mute respectively.

Special Tunings
Non-standard tunings are shown as 'tuning boxes'. Each box represents one guitar string, the leftmost box corresponding to the lowest pitched string. The symbol '•' in a box means the pitch of the corresponding string is not altered. A note within a box means the string must be re-tuned as stated. For tablature readers, numbers appear in the boxes. The numbers represent the number of half-steps the string must be tuned up or down. The tablature relates to an instrument tuned as stated.

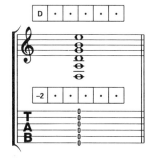

Tune the low E (6th) string down one tone (two half-steps) to D.

Chord naming
The following chord naming convention has been used. Altered 5ths are shown as 'dim5' or 'aug5', whilst alterations to added notes are indicated by '♯' or '♭'.

Where there is no appropriate chord box, for example when the music consists of a repeated figure (or riff) the tonal base is indicated in parenthesis: [C]

Where it was not possible to transcribe a passage, the symbol ∿ appears.

Breaking Into Heaven

Words & Music by Squire

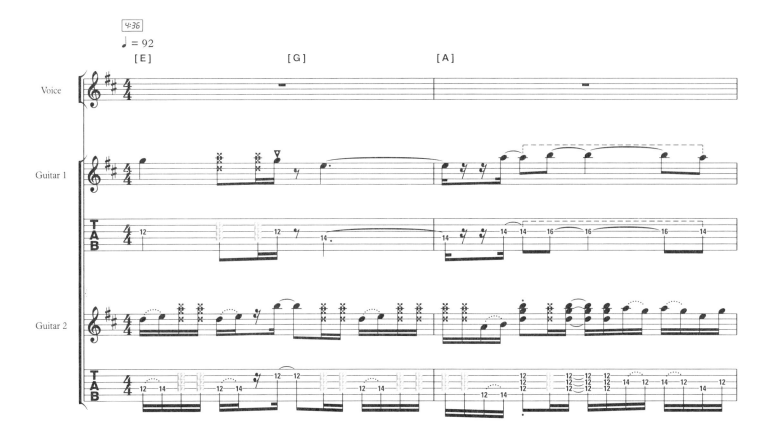

© Copyright 1994 Sony Music Publishing Limited, 10 Great Marlborough Street, London W1.
All Rights Reserved. International Copyright Secured.

when I'm hav - ing it rough, or just__ get - ting old.__

Lis - ten up__ sweet child of mine, have I____ got news for you,__ no -

- bo - dy leaves this place a - live,__ they'll die and join the queue.

Bet - ter man the bar - ri - cades, I'm com-ing in___ to - night,
Hea - ven's gates won't hold me, I'll saw those suck-ers down,

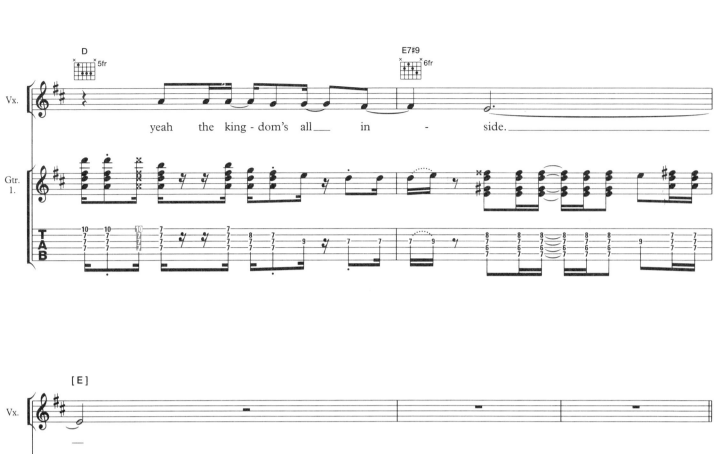

yeah the king-dom's all___ in - side.___

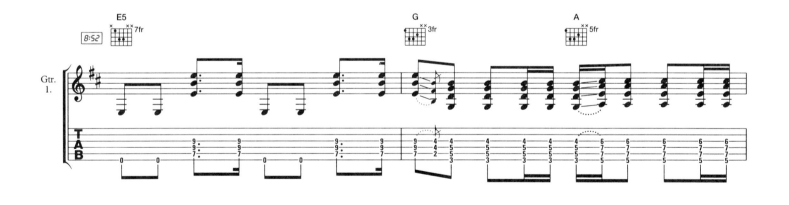

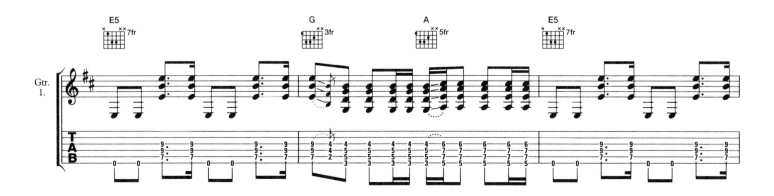

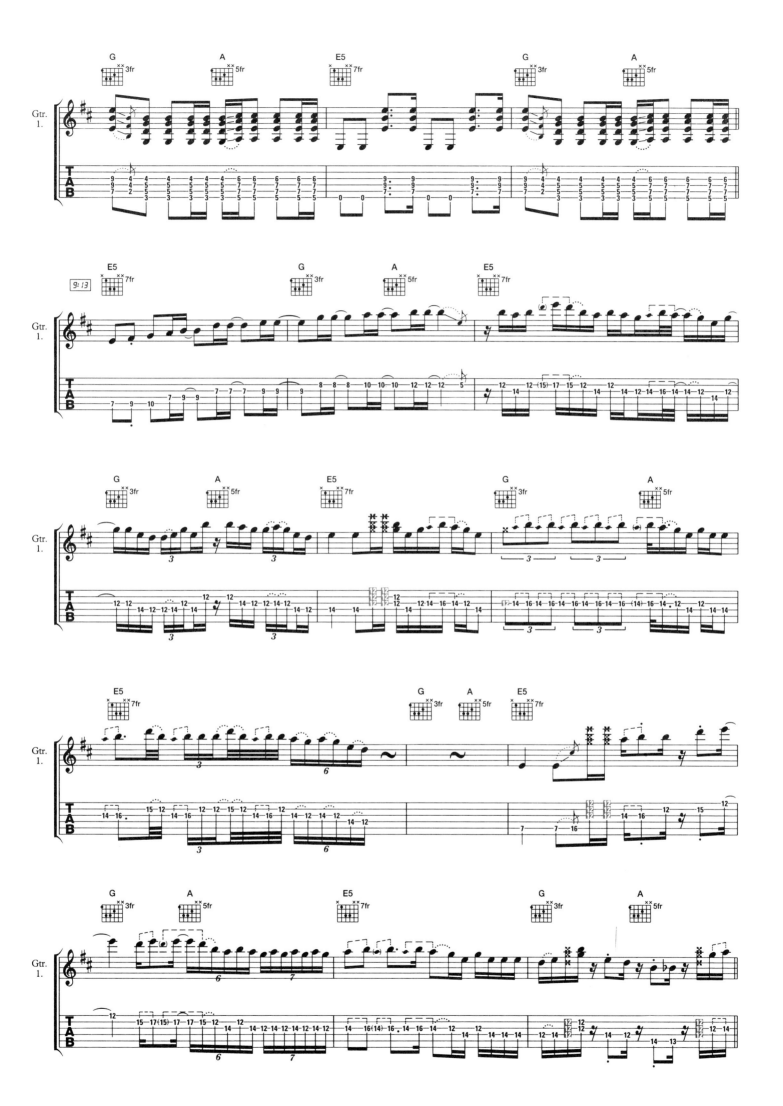

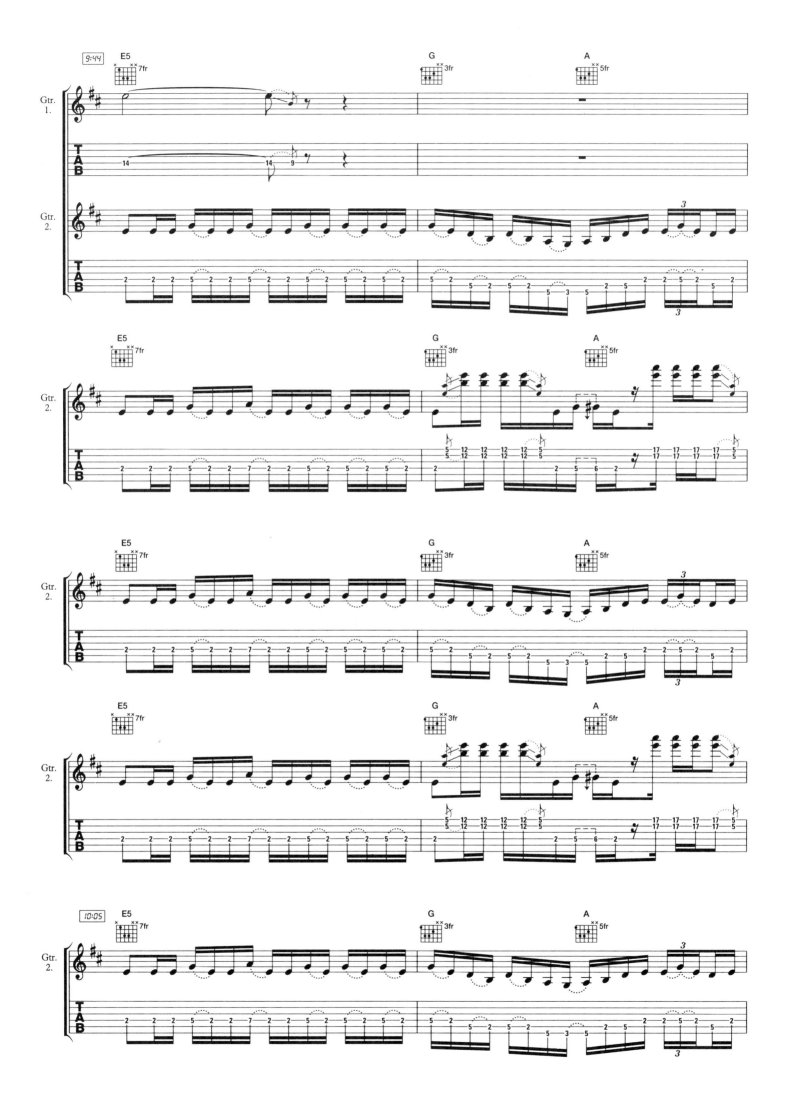

21

Driving South

Words & Music by Squire

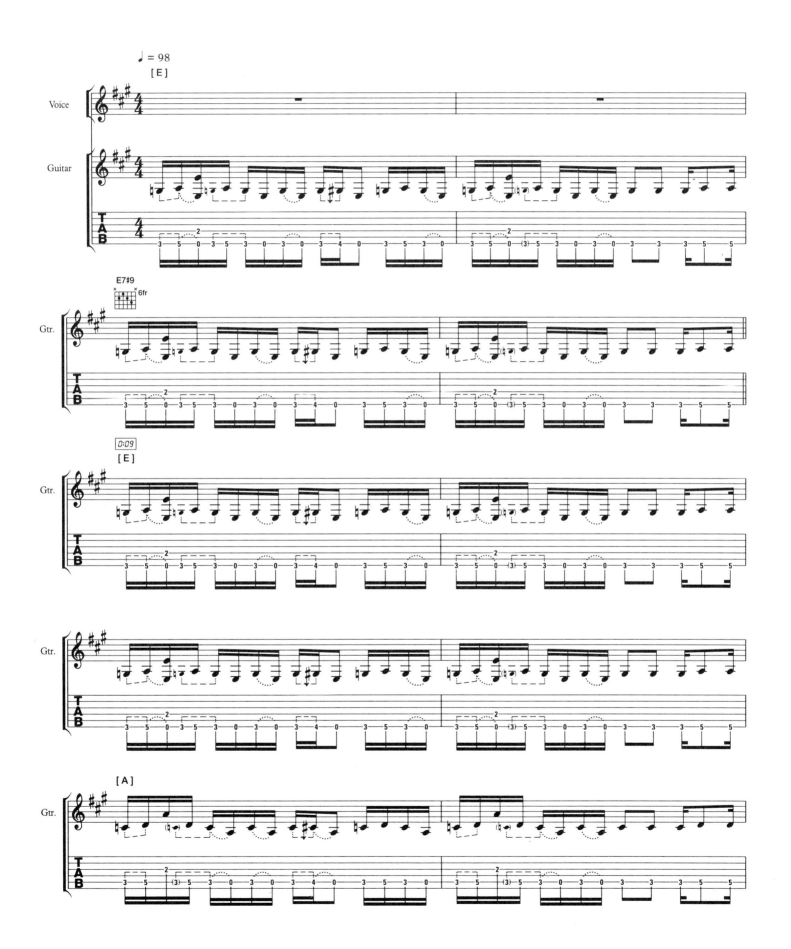

© Copyright 1994 Sony Music Publishing Limited, 10 Great Marlborough Street, London W1.
All Rights Reserved. International Copyright Secured.

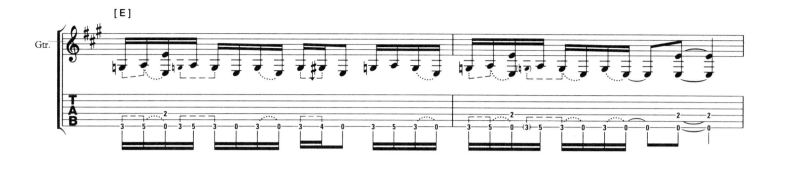

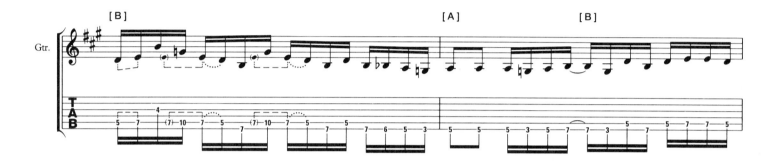

1. Driv - ing south round mid - night, man, I must have been in - sane,

(2.3.) __ not tryin' to make you, I don't want to touch your skin, __

driv-

I __

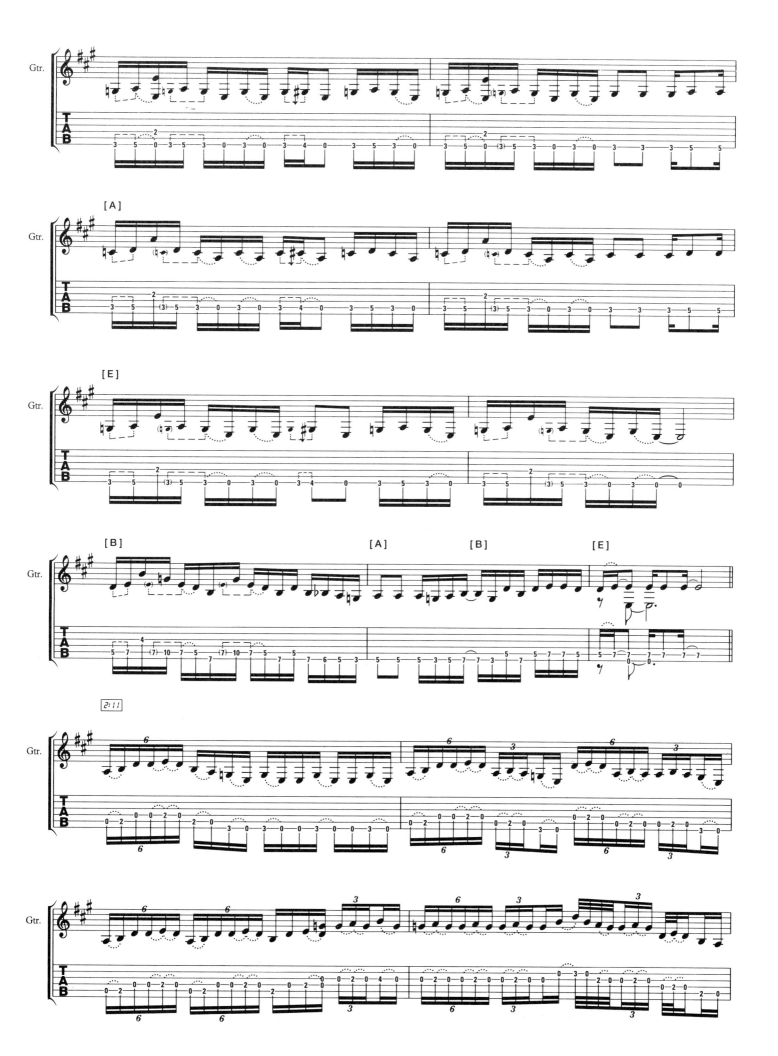

28

-ly old___ cross - road,   he said, 'I'm go-ing no - where,___ I'm

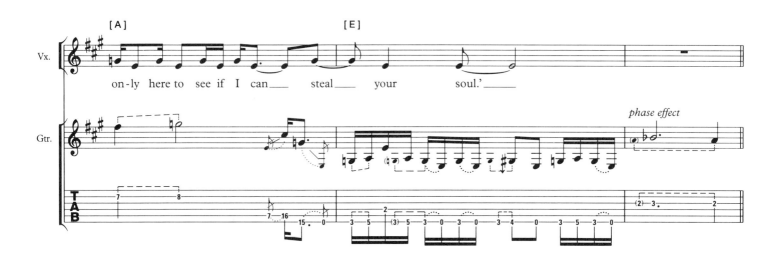

on-ly here to see if I can___ steal___ your   soul.'___

phase effect

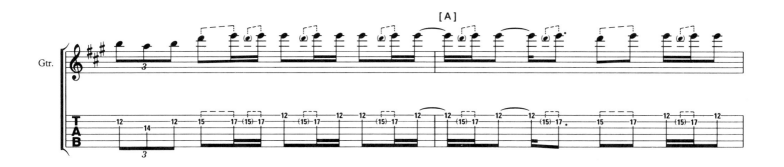

Ten Storey Love Song

Words & Music by Squire

© Copyright 1994 Sony Music Publishing Limited, 10 Great Marlborough Street, London W1.
All Rights Reserved. International Copyright Secured.

-ing e-nough for two.____
___ up, and see___ the light.____

Ten stor-ey love___ song, I____ built this___ thing for you,___ ooh.___

___ Who can take___ you high - er than___ twin peak moun-tain_____ blue?___ Oh well, I

to Coda

built this___ thing for you,___ and I love you true.

2. There's no

34

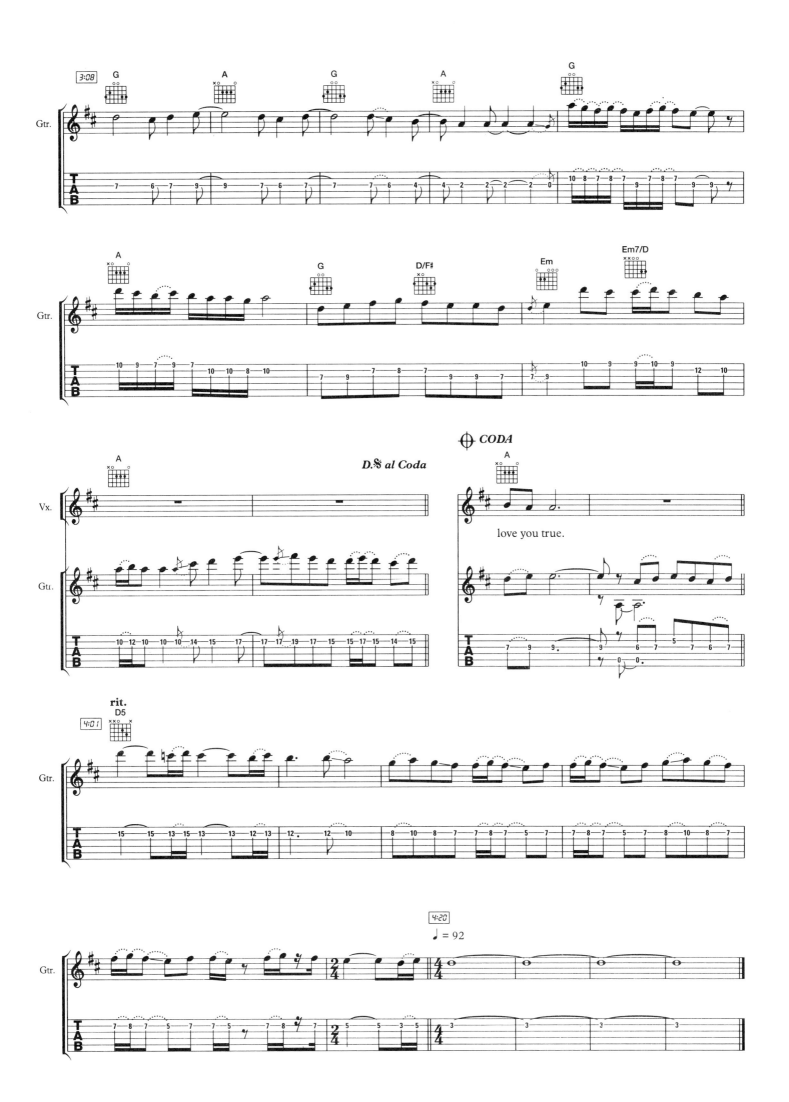

Daybreak

Words & Music by Brown/Mountfield/Squire/Wren

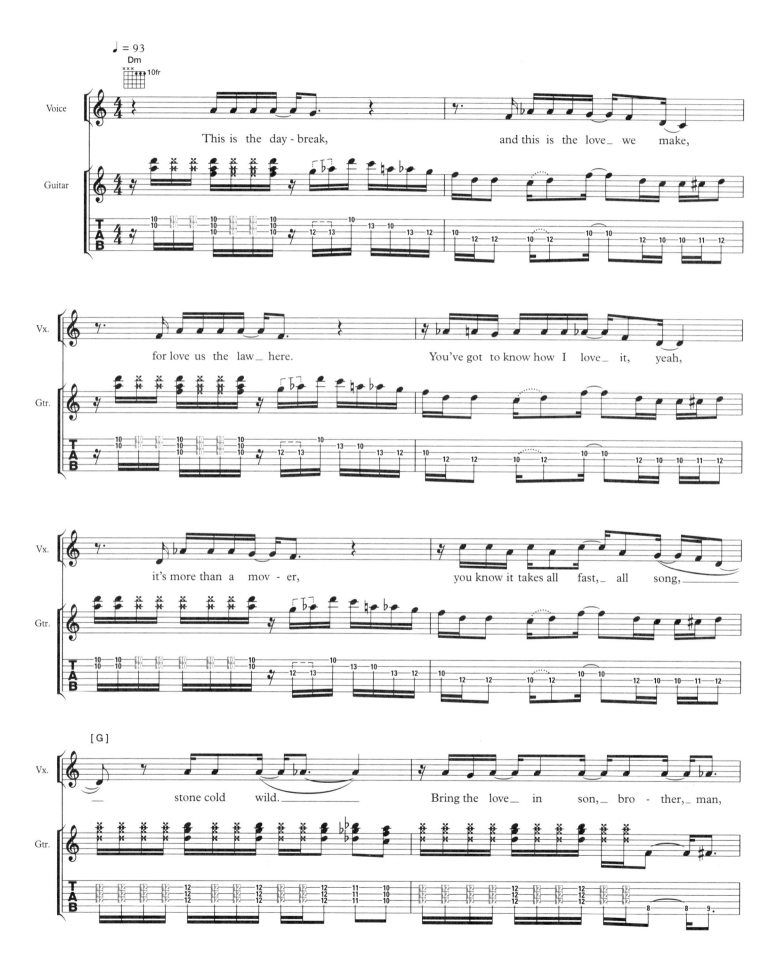

© Copyright 1994 Sony Music Publishing Limited, 10 Great Marlborough Street, London W1.
All Rights Reserved. International Copyright Secured.

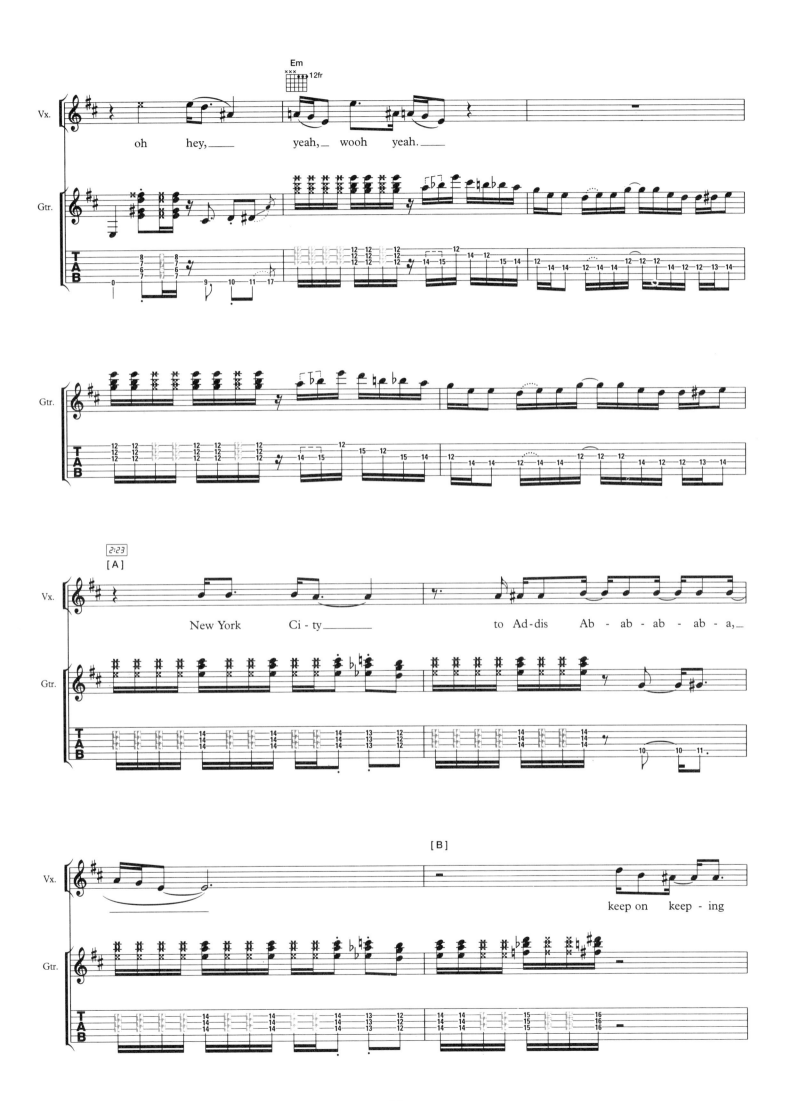

I came to sing this song in your ci-ty.

Ooh,____ for the dream-

- ers,____ one more for the dream-ers,____ yeah.____

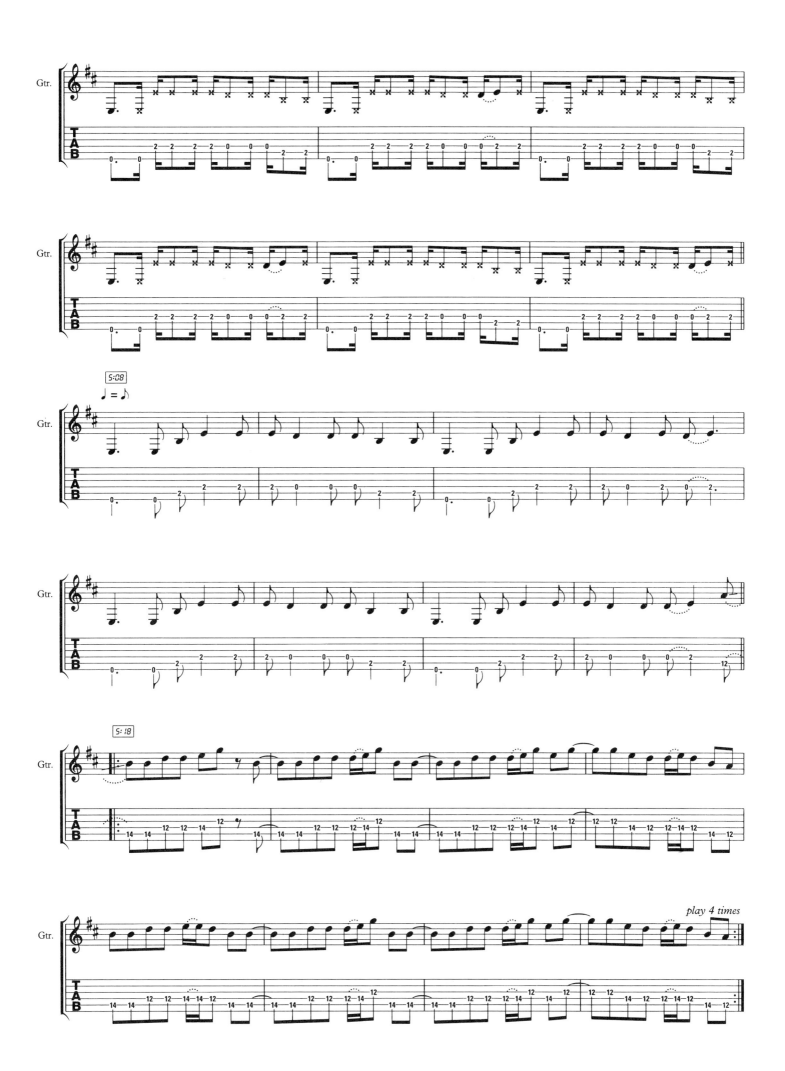

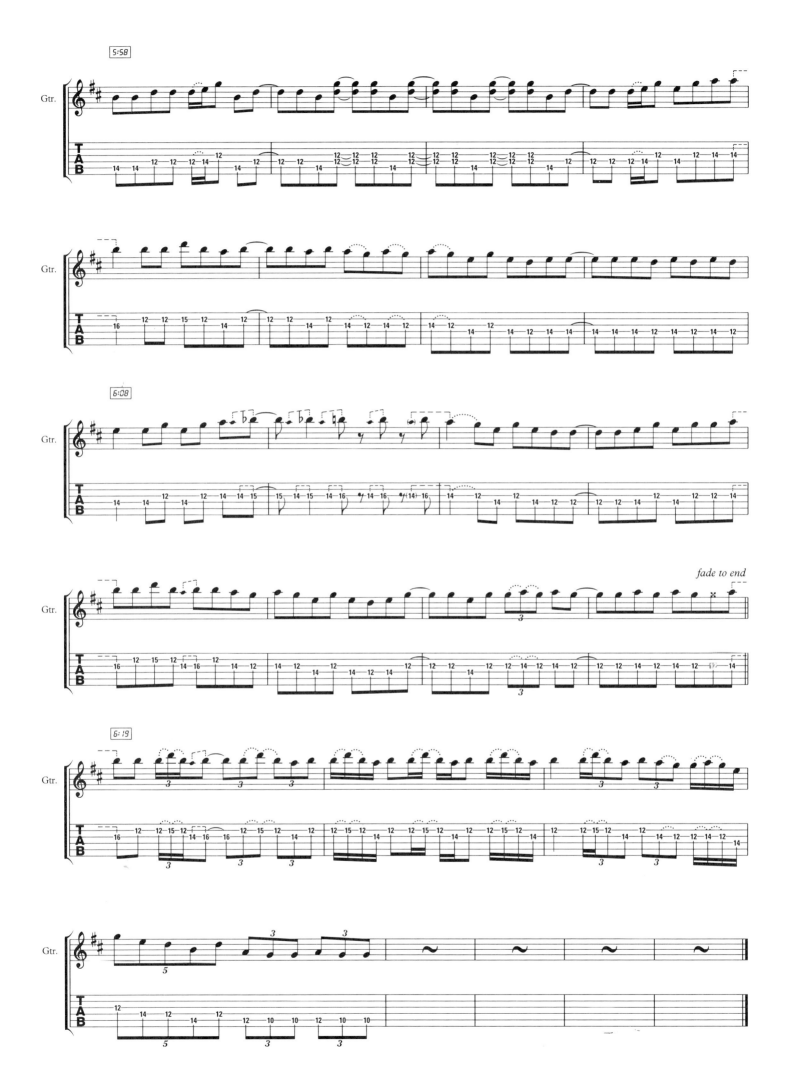

Your Star Will Shine

Words & Music by Squire

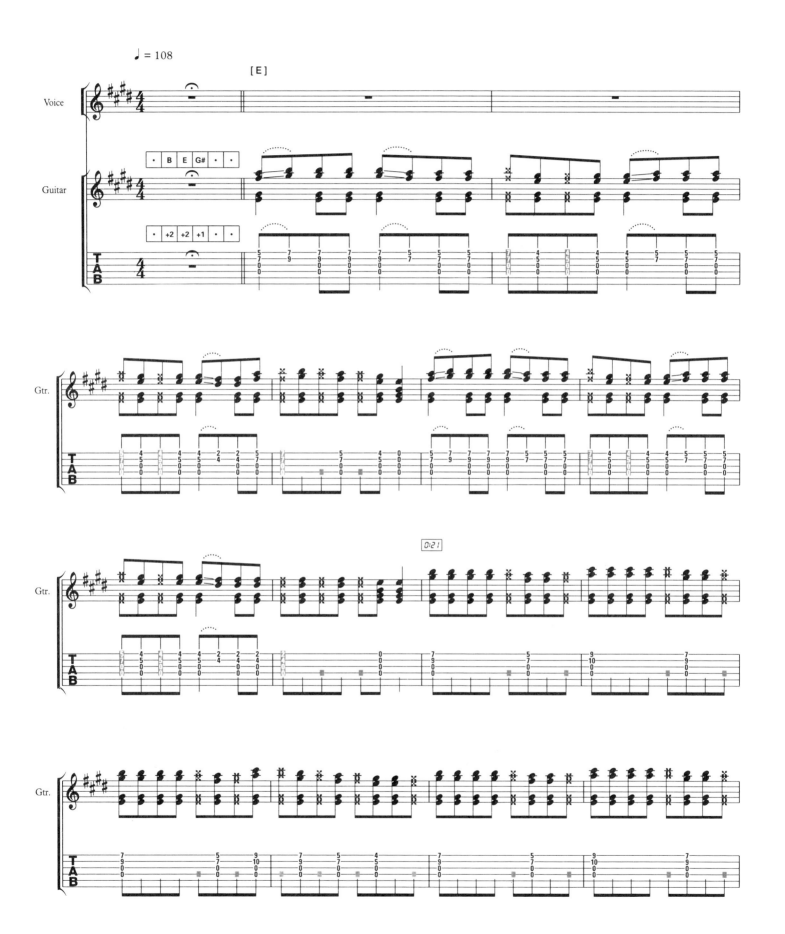

© Copyright 1994 Sony Music Publishing Limited, 10 Great Marlborough Street, London W1.
All Rights Reserved. International Copyright Secured.

Your star__ will shine a - gain__ one day, through

deep blue__ vel - vet____ skies,____ shine for all__ the world__ to see__ the

u - ni - verse__ in__ your__ eyes.____

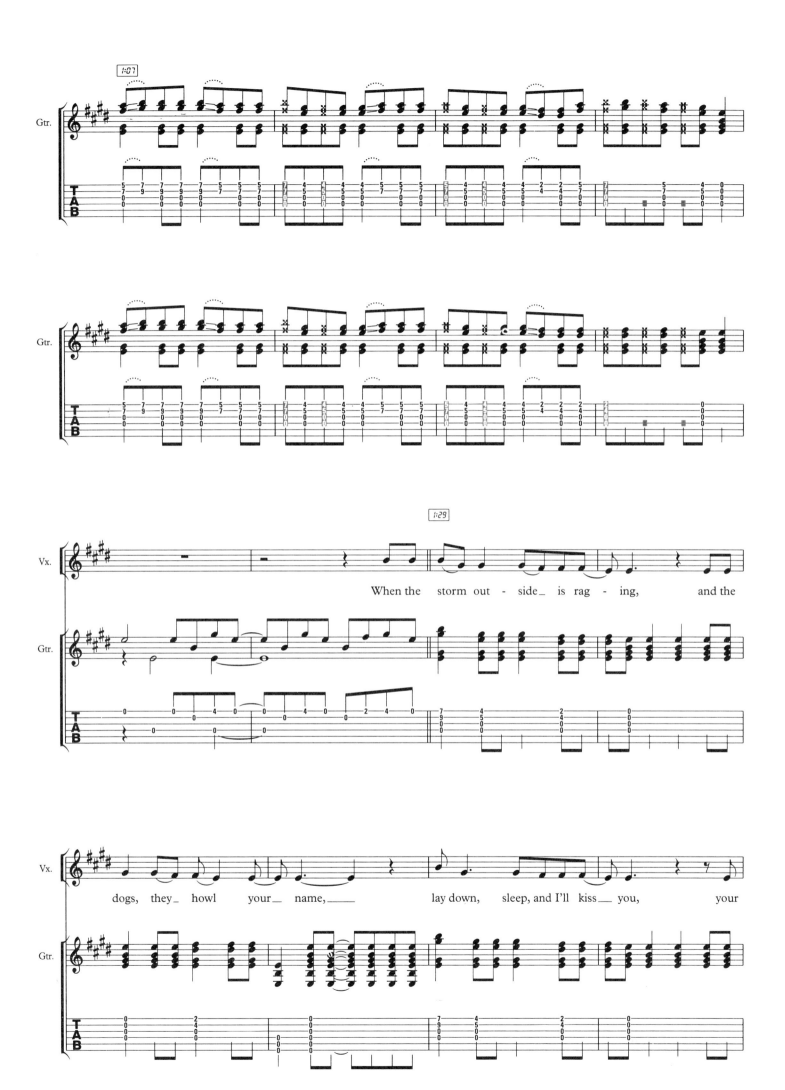

When the storm out - side _ is rag - ing, and the

dogs, they _ howl your _ name, _____ lay down, sleep, and I'll kiss __ you, your

Straight To The Man

Words & Music by Brown

Swing 16th notes (♩ = 92)

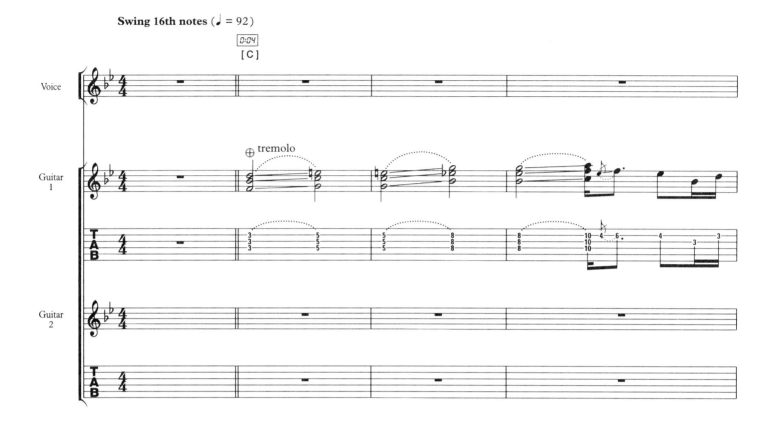

Say-ing this re-ve-la - tion   call de-li-a sta - tion,   an i-ni-ti-a-

© Copyright 1994 Sony Music Publishing Limited, 10 Great Marlborough Street, London W1.
All Rights Reserved. International Copyright Secured.

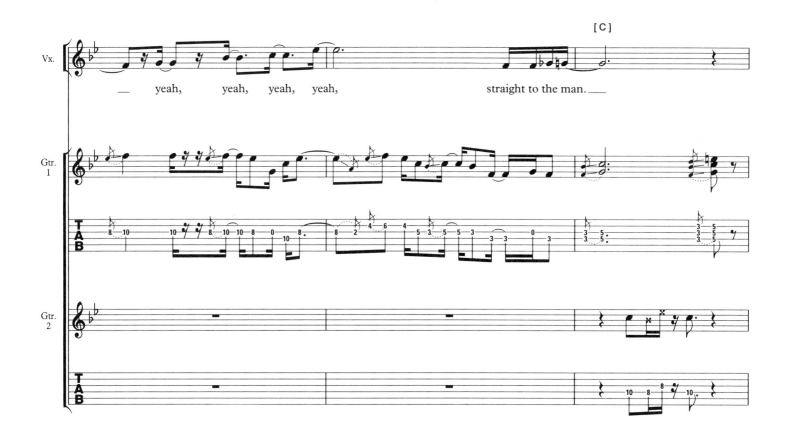

yeah,   yeah,   yeah,   yeah,   straight to the man. ___

On an is-land of tra-

one slip you don't ne-ver for-get, who could ev-er for-get?_ You know I ne-ver for-get.

Do do do,_ do do_ do, do do do do do do do,_ do do do do, straight

to the man.__   Oh, you know they're try-ing to fade_ you.

Saw this re-ve-la-

of Grande Bre - ta - gne owes a debt.

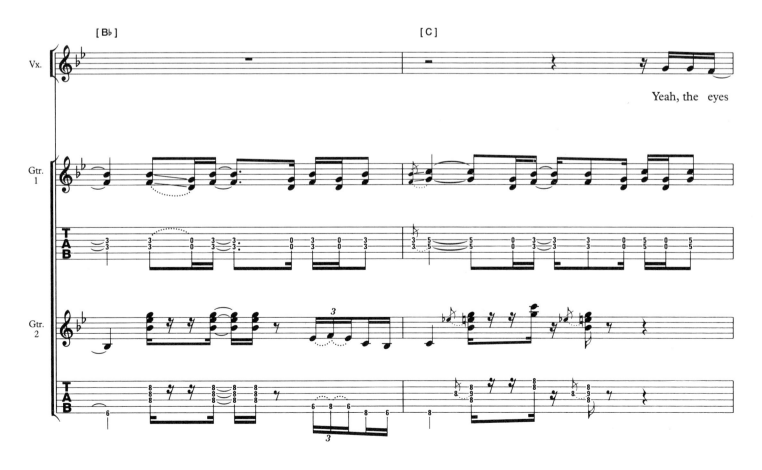

[Bb] [C]

Yeah, the eyes

of Grande Bre - ta - gne   all   eyes__ of Grande Bre - ta - gne

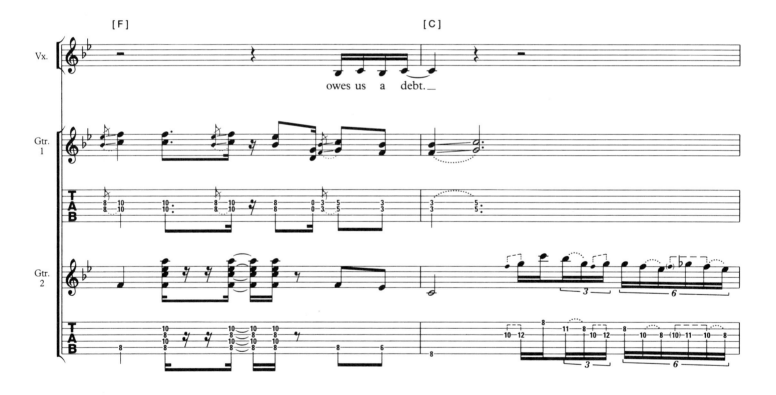

owes us   a   debt.__

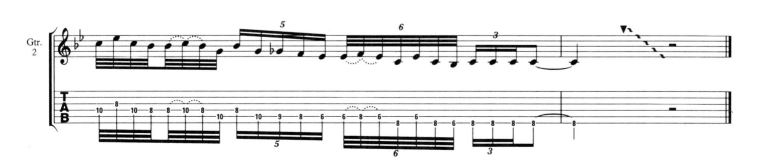

Tightrope

Words & Music by Squire

© Copyright 1994 Sony Music Publishing Limited, 10 Great Marlborough Street, London W1.
All Rights Reserved. International Copyright Secured.

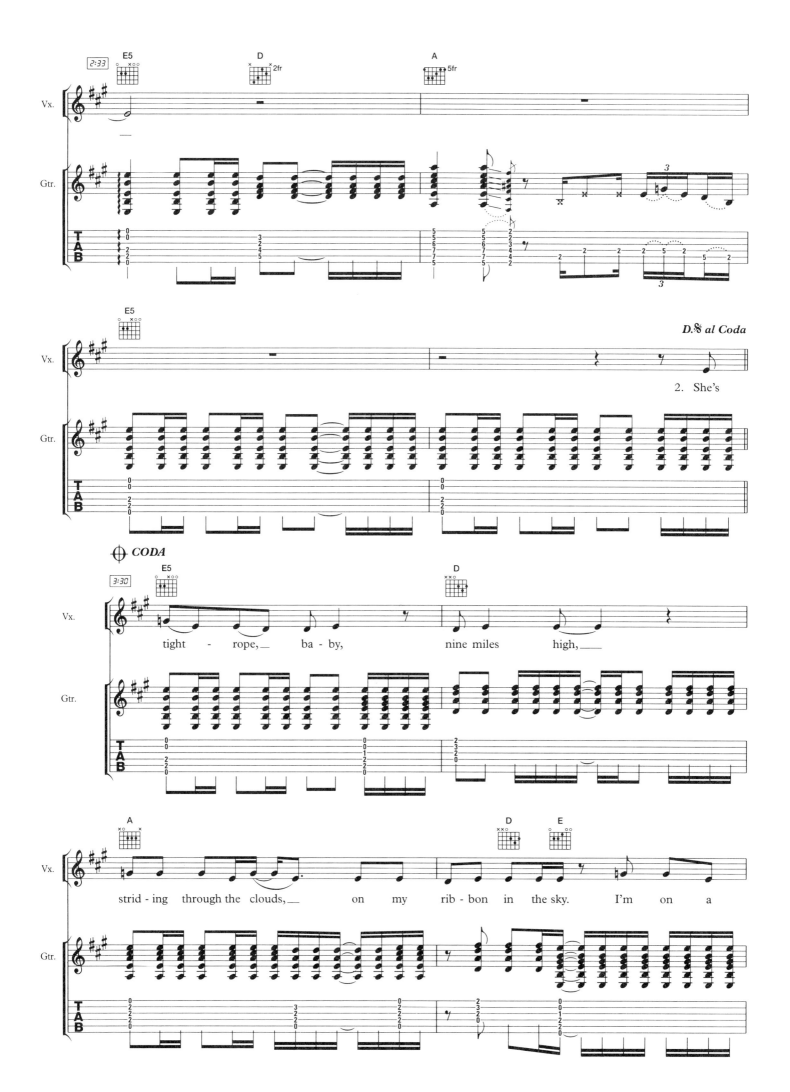

Begging You

Words & Music by Squire/Brown

© Copyright 1994 Sony Music Publishing Limited, 10 Great Marlborough Street, London W1.
All Rights Reserved. International Copyright Secured.

Here is a warn -ing, the sky___ will di -vide,___ since I

Weigh it and say__ it, is it all in a name, does it call__ you or maul you and drive__ you in-sane. Can it

make you re-mem-ber, time__ is in place, now I'm bell-ing you,___ I'm

beg-ging you. The fly on the coach-wheel told__ me that he got it and he

Good Times

Words & Music by Squire

© Copyright 1994 Sony Music Publishing Limited, 10 Great Marlborough Street, London W1.
All Rights Reserved. International Copyright Secured.

Come on, come on___ now, ba - by, let___ the good times roll a - gain,___ yeah.

Where did our sweet___ love go?___ Who stole a - way___ our time?
How ma - ny days___ have I___ been ly - ing on___ my back_

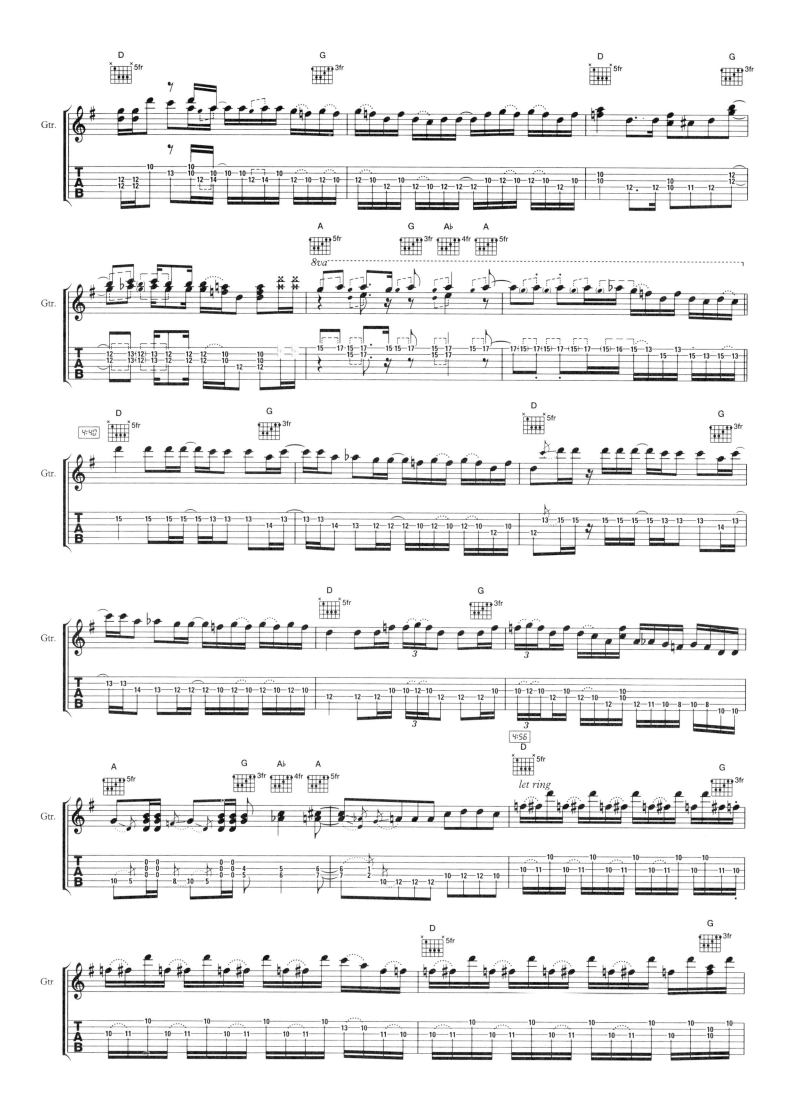

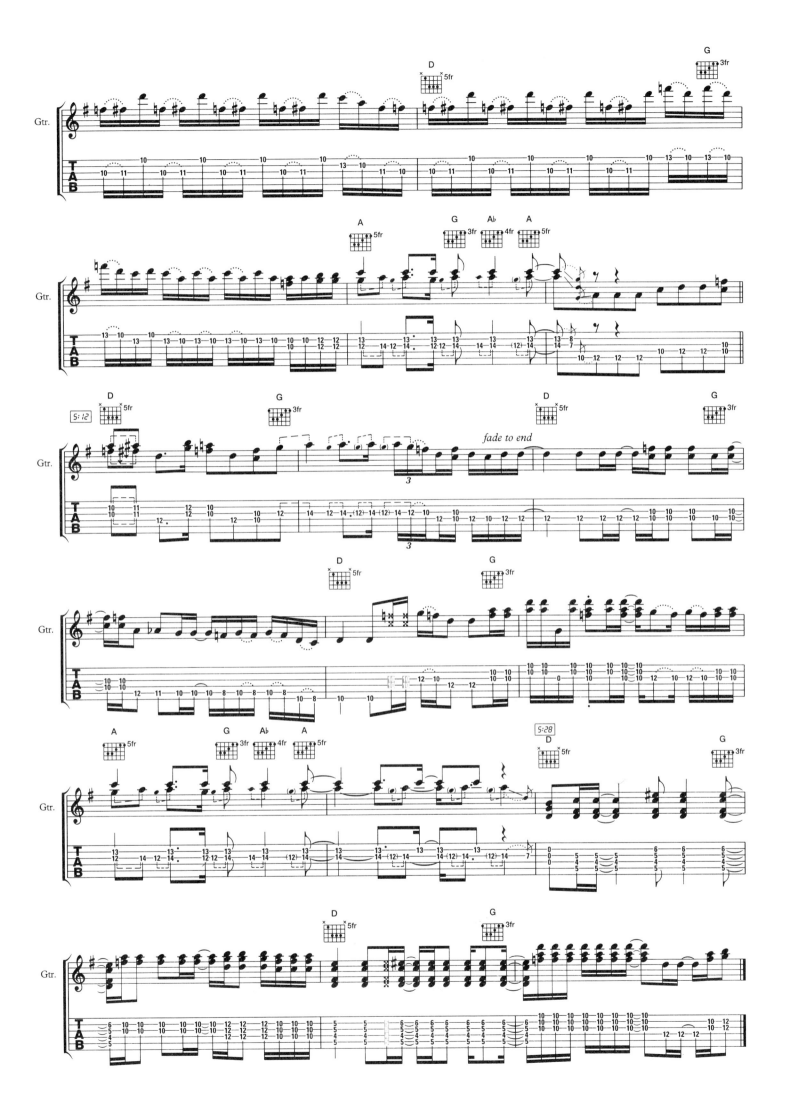

How Do You Sleep

Words & Music by Squire

© Copyright 1994 Sony Music Publishing Limited, 10 Great Marlborough Street, London W1.
All Rights Reserved. International Copyright Secured.

shin - ing sil - ver sal - ver__ so taste - ful - ly pow - dered with the

fi - nest mi - li - tary quick lime.__

1. Now

Tears

Words & Music by Squire

1. Our love,____ girl, is go-ing____ through____ chan - ges,
2. Lost in a maze____ of my_____ own____ mak - ing,

© Copyright 1994 Sony Music Publishing Limited, 10 Great Marlborough Street, London W1.
All Rights Reserved. International Copyright Secured.

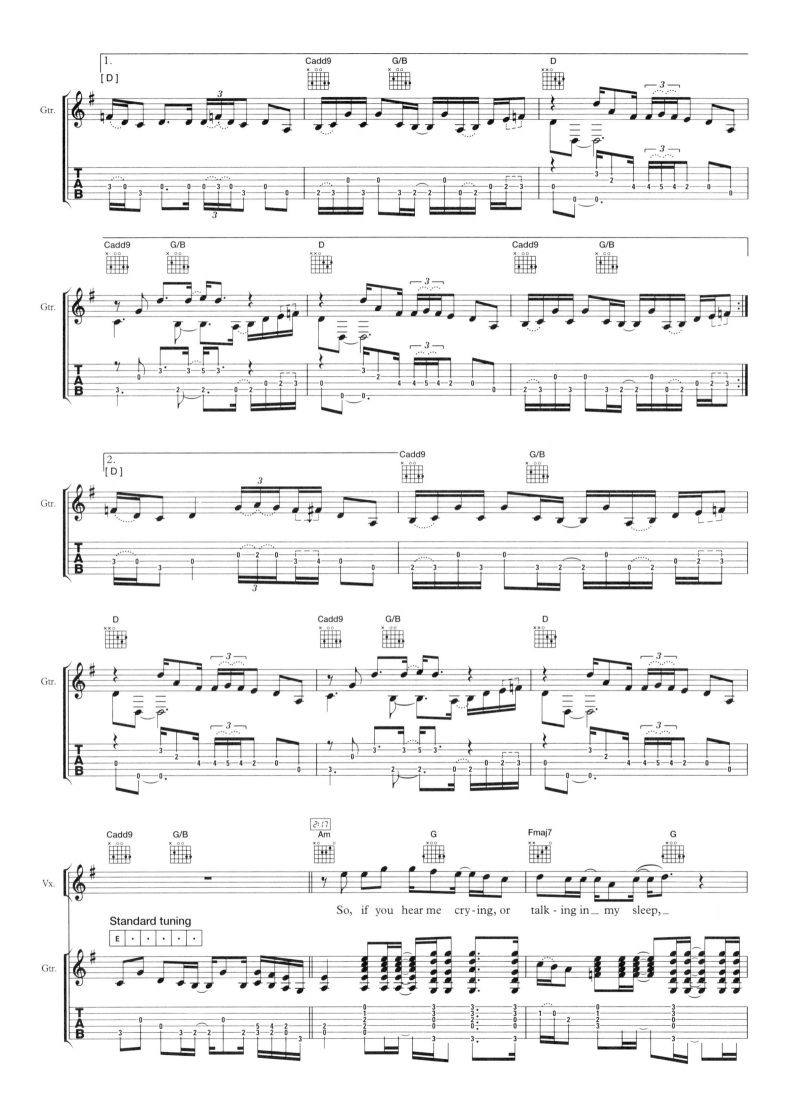

So, if you hear me cry-ing, or talk-ing in__ my sleep,__

Standard tuning

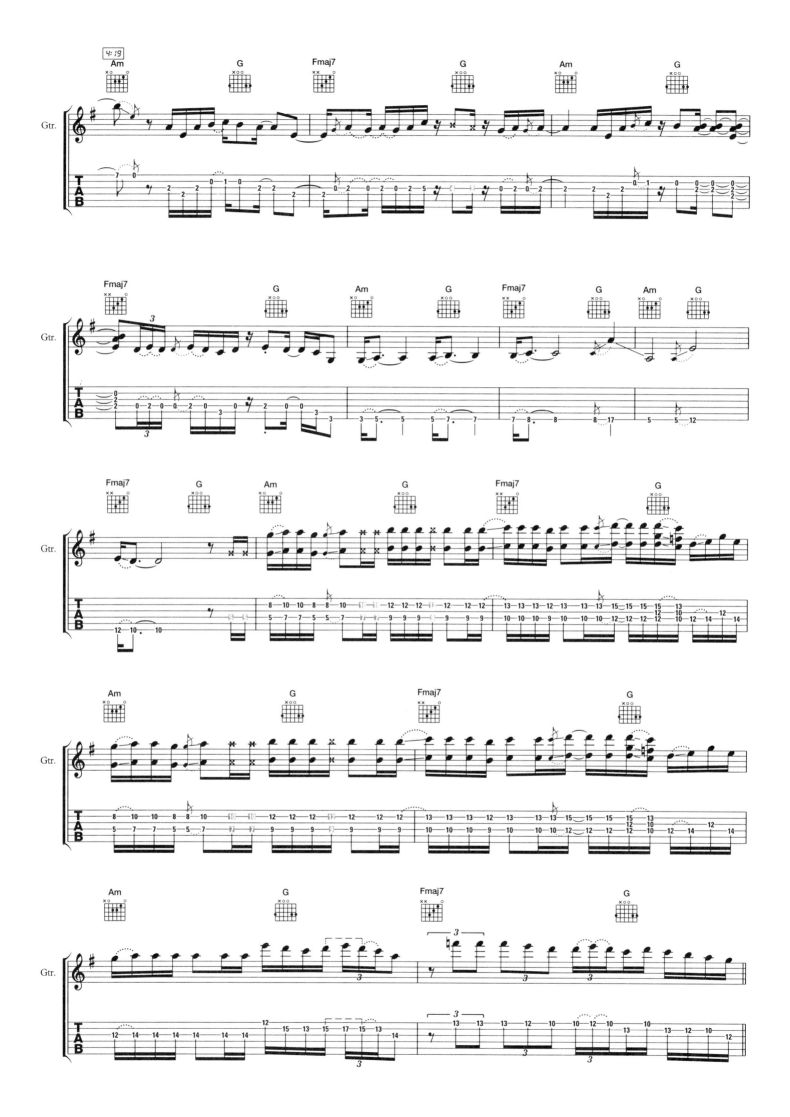

I've seen the fu - ture in ___ the tracks _____ of ___ your _____ tears, _____

of ___ your ___ tears, ___   of ___ your ___ tears. ___

Vx. lyrics:
I cast a short-er sha-dow with ev - ery pass-ing day,_____ no time to think,_ I'm_ just_

_ fad-ing a - way. Some kind of ma - gic_ in all_ your hopes and fears,_____

shows me the fu - ture through the tracks_____ of_ your___ tears._

repeat ad lib. to fade

Love Spreads

Words & Music by Squire

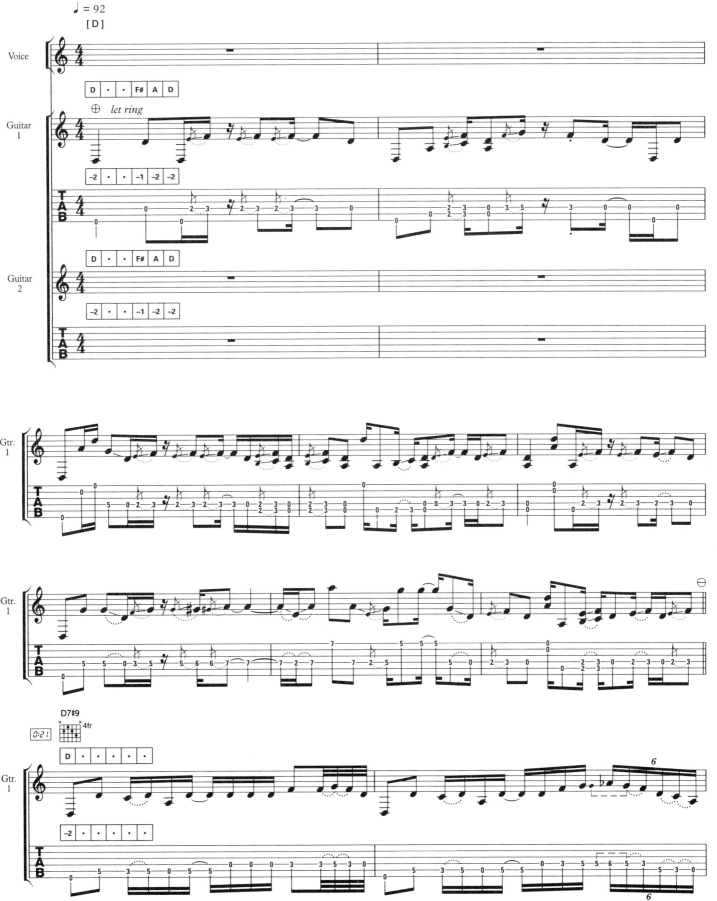

© Copyright 1994 Sony Music Publishing Limited, 10 Great Marlborough Street, London W1.
All Rights Reserved. International Copyright Secured.

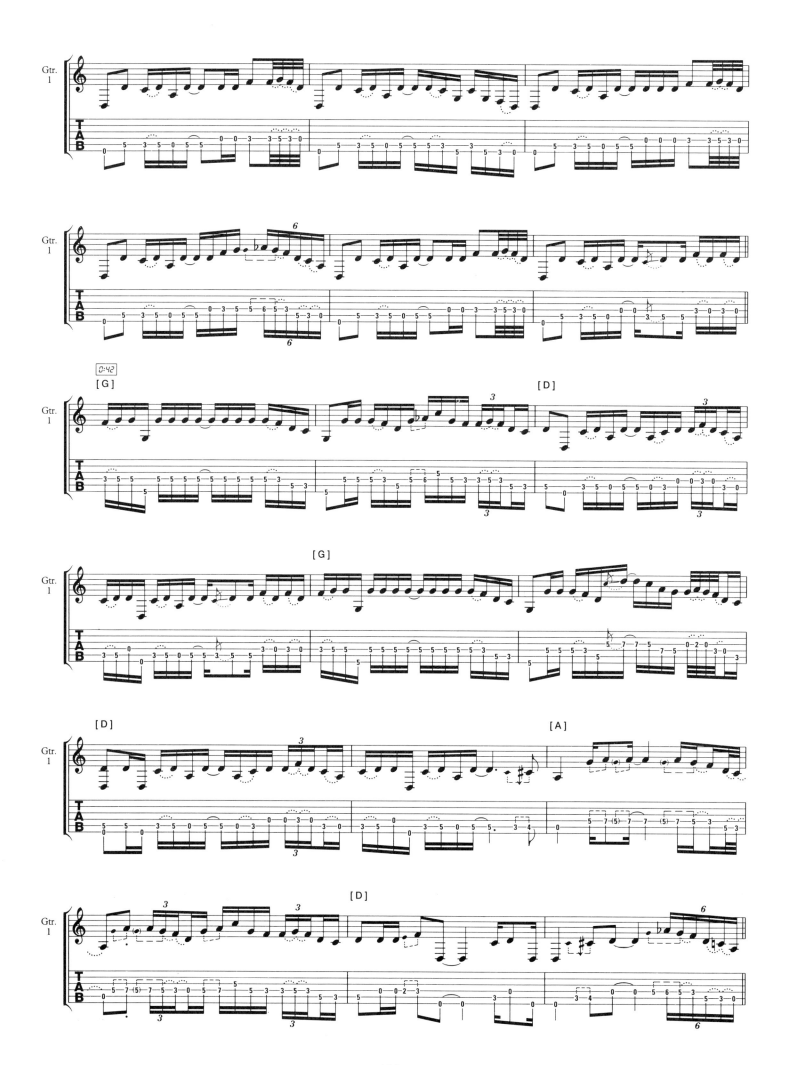

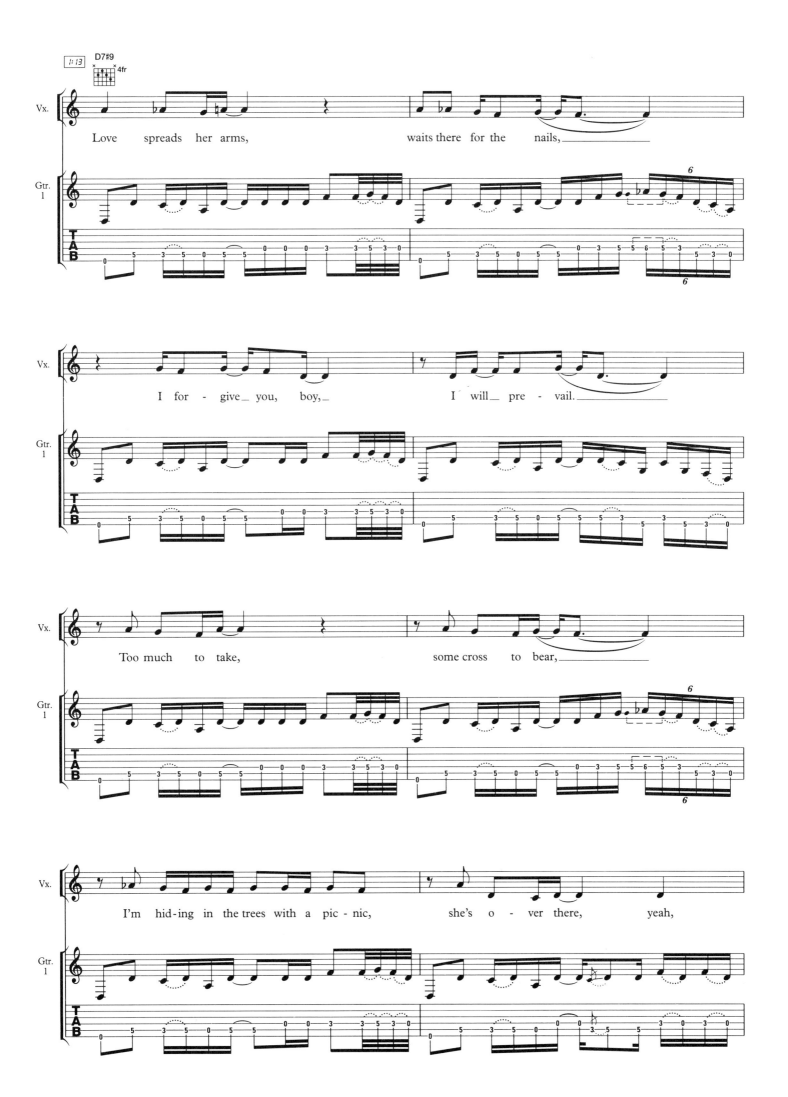

She did-n't scream,___ she did-n't make a sound,_____

'I for-give__ you, boy,'__ but don't leave town._____

Cold black skin, na-ked in the rain,_____

ham-mer flash in the light - ning,_____ they're hurt - ing her a - gain.

Let me put you in the pic - ture, let me show you what I mean, the mes - si -

- ah is_____ my sis - ter, ain't no king,___ man, she's my queen. Let me

She did-n't scream, she did-n't make a sound,___ 'I for-give you, boy,' but don't leave town. ___

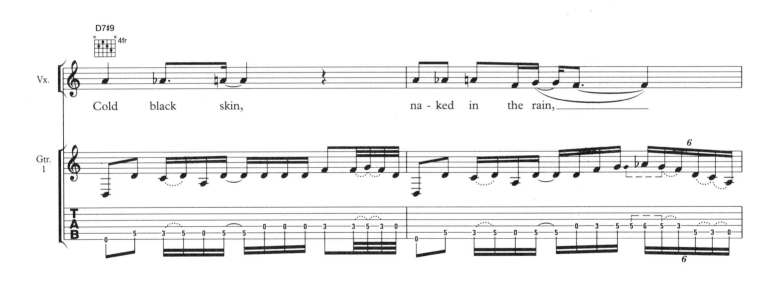

Cold black skin, na - ked in the rain,_____

ham-mer flash in the light - ning,_____ they're hurt - ing her a - gain.

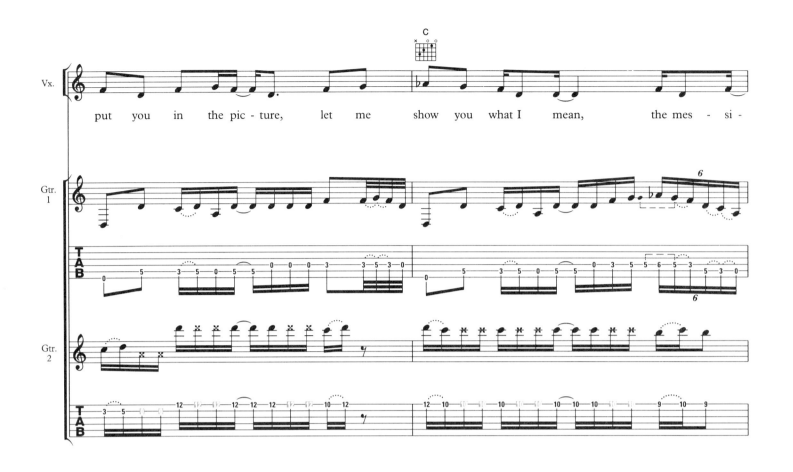

put you in the pic - ture, let me show you what I mean, the mes - si -

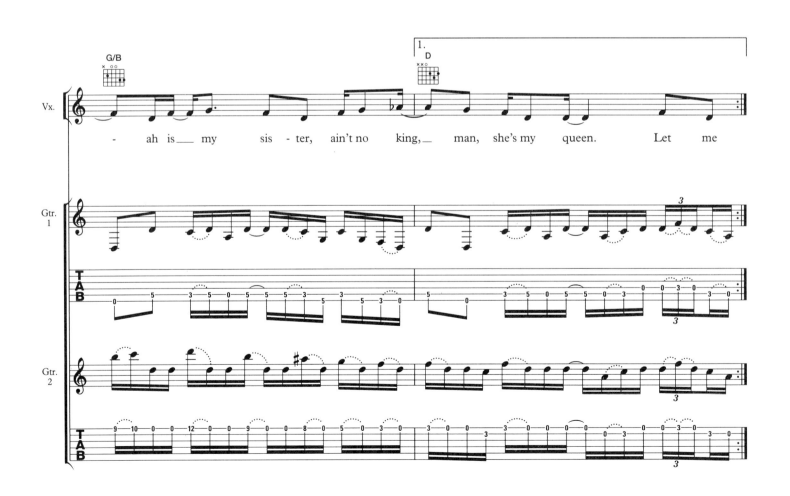

- ah is__ my sis - ter, ain't no king,__ man, she's my queen. Let me

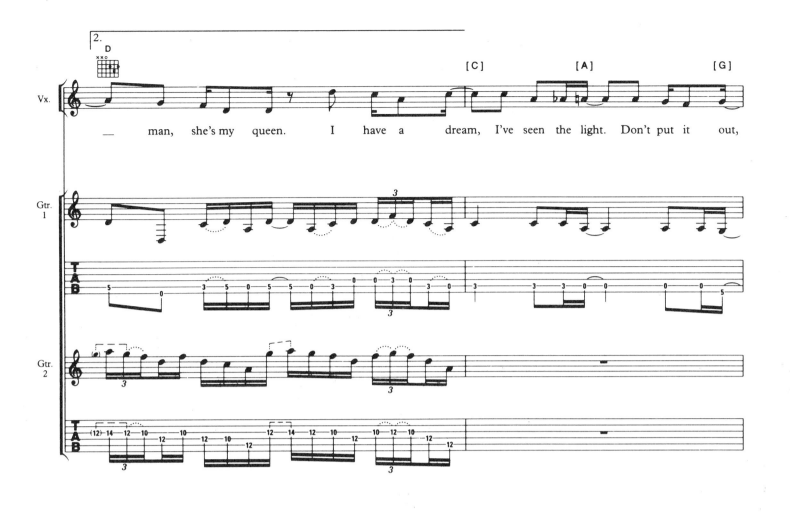

man, she's my queen. I have a dream, I've seen the light. Don't put it out,

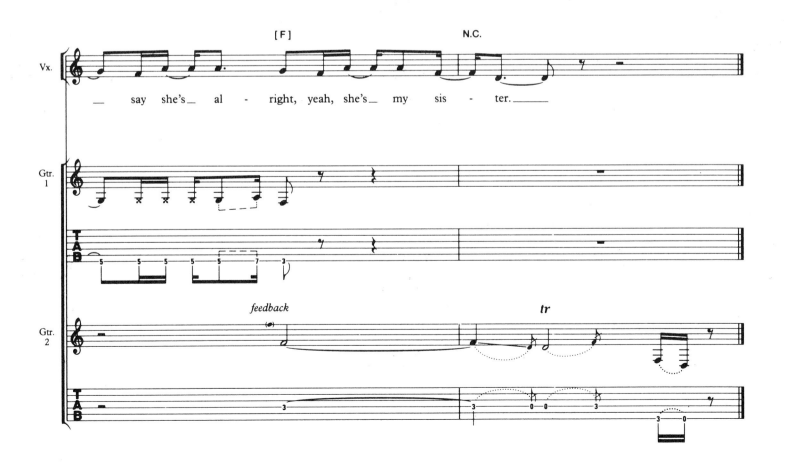

say she's_ al - right, yeah, she's_ my sis - ter.___

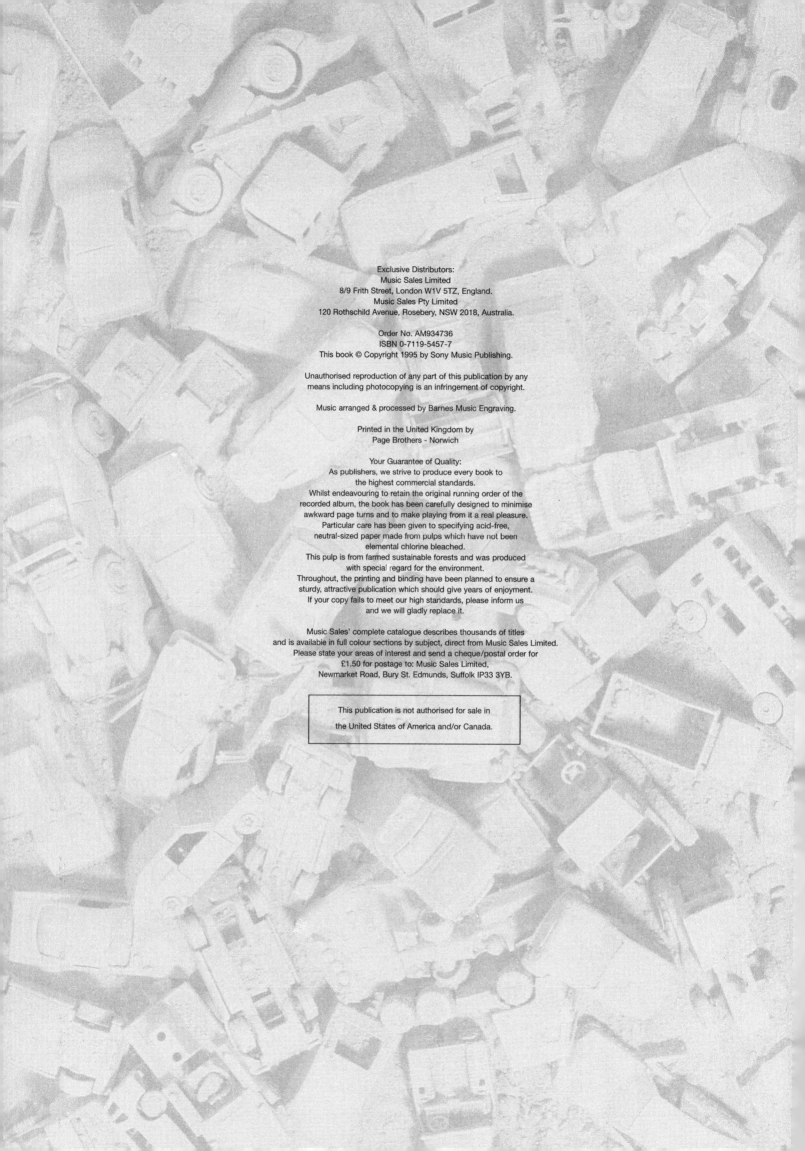

Exclusive Distributors:
Music Sales Limited
8/9 Frith Street, London W1V 5TZ, England.
Music Sales Pty Limited
120 Rothschild Avenue, Rosebery, NSW 2018, Australia.

Order No. AM934736
ISBN 0-7119-5457-7
This book © Copyright 1995 by Sony Music Publishing.

Unauthorised reproduction of any part of this publication by any
means including photocopying is an infringement of copyright.

Music arranged & processed by Barnes Music Engraving.

Printed in the United Kingdom by
Page Brothers - Norwich

Your Guarantee of Quality:
As publishers, we strive to produce every book to
the highest commercial standards.
Whilst endeavouring to retain the original running order of the
recorded album, the book has been carefully designed to minimise
awkward page turns and to make playing from it a real pleasure.
Particular care has been given to specifying acid-free,
neutral-sized paper made from pulps which have not been
elemental chlorine bleached.
This pulp is from farmed sustainable forests and was produced
with special regard for the environment.
Throughout, the printing and binding have been planned to ensure a
sturdy, attractive publication which should give years of enjoyment.
If your copy fails to meet our high standards, please inform us
and we will gladly replace it.

Music Sales' complete catalogue describes thousands of titles
and is available in full colour sections by subject, direct from Music Sales Limited.
Please state your areas of interest and send a cheque/postal order for
£1.50 for postage to: Music Sales Limited,
Newmarket Road, Bury St. Edmunds, Suffolk IP33 3YB.

This publication is not authorised for sale in
the United States of America and/or Canada.